21,4661

D1106337

DOG
ALMIGHTY!

JOHN DONEGAN

HOWELL
BOOK HOUSE INC.

First published 1987 in the United States by
Howell Book House Inc., 230 Park Avenue, New York, N.Y. 10169

Most of the cartoons in this book have previously appeared in
Punch and are reproduced by kind permission of the
proprietors, Punch Publications Ltd

First published 1986 by Souvenir Press Ltd,
43 Great Russell Street, London WC1B 3PA
and simultaneously in Canada

ISBN 0 87605 466 1

Photoset and printed in Great Britain by
Redwood Burn Limited, Trowbridge, Wiltshire

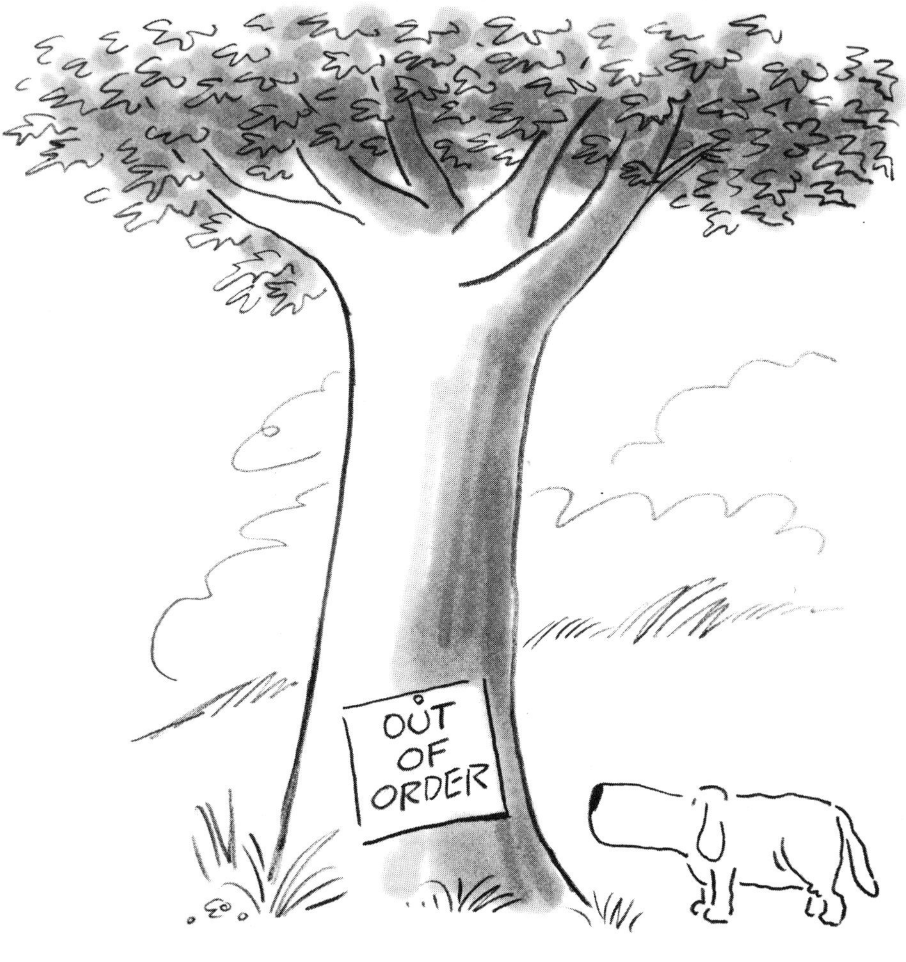
OUT
OF
ORDER

'It doesn't have to grab you — just eat it!'

'Why wait till Father's Day? Give it to him now.'

'Stand perfectly still! One false move and he'll faint.'

'He's not always so friendly with total strangers, but then
he's not always drunk.'

'There's a furry thing in here eating cheese. I understand
that's your department.'

'Clear off, or I'll set my stockbroker on you.'

'Yes, yes, I'm yours, body and soul! Now can I watch Clive James?'

'Merciful Heaven, Winston! Where *did* you learn to tango like that?'

'Do I hear the merry clink of ice on Waterford?'

'Kill!'

'Would you mind if Rocky and I discussed this alone, Arthur?'

'Go and see what's bothering him. He doesn't usually howl for nothing.'

'Margaret thinks it makes him look dependable.'

'He's very gentle, but prey to uncontrollable fits of the giggles.'

'Contrary to popular mythology, I never actually said "Play it again, Sam".'

'You're kidding! Just that and they *feed* you!'

'. . . and finally a word from Lloyd on security.'

'Here's the fifty thousand. Now hand over the cat.'

'No, you may *not* be tried by twelve good dogs and true.'

'So I'm hypnotised. So what?'

'My God, you'd better go! He'll be home any minute.'

'Don't be silly, Tarquin. Nobody elopes any more.'

'Mac's the name, thirty-two pounds of lightning reaction and compact muscle.
I don't scare easy or suffer fools gladly. Remember that and
we'll all have a nice time.'

'Okay, but be quick about it!'

'Negotiate? What is there to negotiate?'

'Go ahead, organise a union. I'll organise the new potatoes, the garden peas and the mint sauce.'

'Well, of *course* I'm surprised — I'm usually ignored at parties.'

'It's amazing! You look so small on television.'

'You see? He's a different dog when he smiles.'

'Well, I've been in three or four documentaries, two feature films, and loads of commercials, of course. Mostly as a dog.'

'For Heaven's sake! Pay it, or make a scene. One or the other.'

'The fact is, Leonard, I'm not your real father.'

'More colour, more! He likes lots and lots of colour.'

'*Must* you go home? Why not stay the night?'

'I still say it's unusual for a spaniel to leave home.'

'... and a sausage and a small scotch for him.'

'The usual? I serve six hundred drinks a day and I'm supposed to remember "the usual"?'

'You don't *look* eighteen.'

'Wouldn't have such a thing as a swizzle stick, I suppose?'

'That's Marcus in his prime — proud, arrogant and top of the heap, yet tenderness itself with his loved ones. I forget who the man is.'

'It's awful. The place seems so empty without him.'

JULIUS II
1962–1974